a story abre

by salvatore iaquinta
drawings by Diane Amil

PCP
Perfect Canine Products
a division of
Purely Chaotic Publishing
copyright 2021

To Vivian
and everyone who loves a pet.

Everyone should have a dog.

Sitting people.

Standing people.

Everyone.

Someday, you might have a dog.

He might start as a tiny puppy.

You can train him to ring a bell
when he wants to go potty.

5

He might play frisbee,

chase his tail,

or play hide and seek.

Sometimes he will be
naughty (like you).

He might steal your food

and prance in celebration.

He might bite your plant.
That naughty dog.

If he gets sick you will worry.

That worry is love.
(He will get better soon).

Then he will chase his splashes.

And hunt invisible animals

until he is so tired he cannot move.

He will bark at birds,

but never catch one.

He will mark the neighborhood

and sniff other dogs.

He will wiggle and waggle when
you come home.

His muzzle will turn gray
as he gets older.

His walks will take longer.

But he will still love a belly rub.

He will stop jumping.

and he will sleep more.

Someday he will not wake up.

All things die.
Flowers die quickly.

The dinosaurs died
a long time ago.

It is sad. It is okay to cry.

That is love.

You will smile again when you
remember the fun you had.

Like the time you chased him

and he chased you.

Every day is a gift from
your dog to you.

You can remember
your dog forever.

A dog teaches you that
love is limitless.

Everyone should have a dog.

• • •

Sometimes a book ends.
Sometimes only a chapter ends.

Someday there might be
another dog. A different dog.

A dog for you to teach

and to wrestle.

A dog you can also love.
Love does not replace love.

Love only adds to love.
Love does not end.

Never
THE END

This book is inspired by Zeppelin, a
true friend for 15 years.

After Zeppelin died I started making this book. A month later the vet told us our other dog, Jinx, had a brain tumor. After feeling miserable and thinking that the world was unfair, I realized so many people suffer the same loss. I created this book to let people know that a dog is a true friend and true friends are always worth having. The sadness of losing that friend is real and even profound. Accepting that inevitable loss is part of life. If this book helps one person get over their hesitancy of getting a dog because of their short lifespan, then it is a success. If this book helps one person cope with the loss of a loved one, then it is a success.

May a four-legged friend enrich your life!

Jinx, taking a break from counter-surfing.
That lovely, naughty dog.

Thanks for reading, reviewing online, and referring all your friends to this book.

Made in the USA
Columbia, SC
11 November 2021